Grade 3

MATH DRILLS

Written by **Shannon Keeley**

Illustrated by **Clive Scruton**

This book belongs to

_____

ISBN-13: 978-1-4114-9903-4
ISBN-10: 1-4114-9903-4

For more information, please visit _www.flashkidsbooks.com_
Please submit changes or report errors to _www.flashkidsbooks.com/errors_

Printed and bound in China

Spark Publishing
120 Fifth Avenue
New York, NY 10011

Dear Parent,

Learning to add, subtract, multiply, and divide are important steps in your child's educational development. This book will help your child learn basic math skills covered in the third grade. Follow these simple steps to make the most of this workbook:

- Find a comfortable place where you and your child can work quietly together.
- Encourage your child to go at his or her own pace.
- Help your child with the problems if he or she needs it.
- Offer lots of praise and support.
- Let your child reward his or her work with the included stickers.
- Most of all, remember that learning should be fun! Enjoy this special time spent together.

Paw Print Path

Add.

Follow the paws to the pet shop.

1.
$$8 \\ +\,4$$

2.
$$6 \\ +\,5$$

3.
$$10 \\ +\,7$$

4.
$$12 \\ +\,6$$

5.
$$22 \\ +\,14$$

6.
$$36 \\ +\,21$$

7.
$$72 \\ +\,26$$

8.
$$33 \\ +\,4$$

9.
$$40 \\ +\,9$$

10.
$$56 \\ +\,32$$

PET shop

PETS

PETS

U.S.

Kitten Code

Subtract the numbers.
Use the letter next to each number to solve the code.

1. $\begin{array}{r} 7 \\ -\ 5 \\ \hline \end{array}$ **F**

2. $\begin{array}{r} 8 \\ -\ 4 \\ \hline \end{array}$ **C**

3. $\begin{array}{r} 6 \\ -\ 5 \\ \hline \end{array}$ **P**

4. $\begin{array}{r} 12 \\ -\ 9 \\ \hline \end{array}$ **T**

5. $\begin{array}{r} 18 \\ -\ 7 \\ \hline \end{array}$ **A**

6. $\begin{array}{r} 25 \\ -\ 4 \\ \hline \end{array}$ **P**

7. $\begin{array}{r} 44 \\ -\ 31 \\ \hline \end{array}$ **R**

8. $\begin{array}{r} 56 \\ -\ 24 \\ \hline \end{array}$ **U**

9. $\begin{array}{r} 68 \\ -\ 43 \\ \hline \end{array}$ **L**

10. $\begin{array}{r} 95 \\ -\ 72 \\ \hline \end{array}$ **R**

11. $\begin{array}{r} 76 \\ -\ 5 \\ \hline \end{array}$ **E**

12. $\begin{array}{r} 34 \\ -\ 12 \\ \hline \end{array}$ **S**

___ ___ ___ ___ ___ ___ ___ ___
1   32   13   23   2   71   4   3

___ ___ ___ ___
21   11   25   22

Aquarium Addition

Add the numbers to complete each table.

+ 4		+ 6		+ 8	
4		3		8	
7		9		5	
5		1		9	
6		2		3	

Pet Puzzle

First, subtract the numbers going across. Then subtract the numbers going down. Then subtract the answers going across and down. The first one is done for you.

14	8	6		26	11	
10	5	5		14	8	
4	3	1				

45	30			32	12	
36	24			21	8	

Birdcage Count

Circle the problems whose answers match the number at the top of the cage.

12

6 + 6

7 + 5

8 + 4

9 + 2

9

3 + 6

4 + 5

8 + 2

2 + 7

8

10 − 2

11 − 4

17 − 9

14 − 6

6

15 − 7

12 − 6

14 − 8

10 − 4

Fishy Fact Families

Use the fact family numbers on the fish to complete the problems.

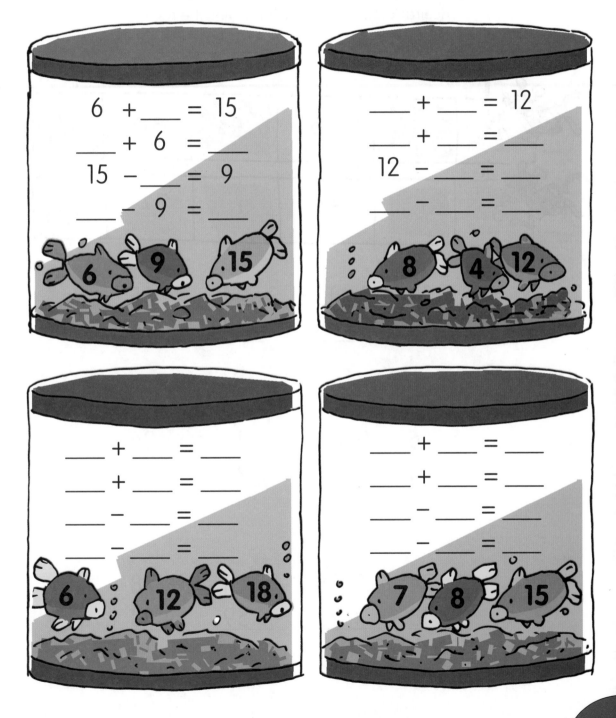

6 + ___ = 15

___ + 6 = ___

15 − ___ = 9

___ − 9 = ___

6   9   15

___ + ___ = 12

___ + ___ = ___

12 − ___ = ___

___ − ___ = ___

8   4   12

___ + ___ = ___

___ + ___ = ___

___ − ___ = ___

___ − ___ = ___

6   12   18

___ + ___ = ___

___ + ___ = ___

___ − ___ = ___

___ − ___ = ___

7   8   15

Rat Race Regrouping

Regroup to solve each problem. As you go, mark off each answer on the racetrack to find out which rat wins the race.

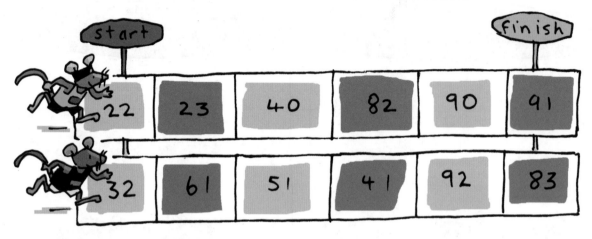

start   finish

22 23 40 82 90 91

32 61 51 41 92 83

1. 13
  + 9

2. 15
  + 8

3. 24
  + 8

4. 55
  + 6

5. 46
  + 5

6. 38
  + 2

7. 15
  + 26

8. 26
  + 56

9. 74
  + 18

10. 58
  + 25

11. 31
  + 59

12. 78
  + 13

Cat Collars

Subtract to solve each problem. Don't forget to regroup!

1.
$$\begin{array}{r} 2\cancel{4}4^{14} \\ -7 \\ \hline 17 \end{array}$$

2.
$$\begin{array}{r} \cancel{4}4^{14} \\ -8 \\ \hline 36 \end{array}$$

3.
$$\begin{array}{r} 2\cancel{6}6^{16} \\ -19 \\ \hline 7 \end{array}$$

4.
$$\begin{array}{r} 6\cancel{5}5^{15} \\ -7 \\ \hline 58 \end{array}$$

5.
$$\begin{array}{r} 5\cancel{3}3^{13} \\ -9 \\ \hline 44 \end{array}$$

6.
$$\begin{array}{r} 4\cancel{6}6^{16} \\ -18 \\ \hline 28 \end{array}$$

7.
$$\begin{array}{r} 3\cancel{5}5^{15} \\ -17 \\ \hline 18 \end{array}$$

8.
$$\begin{array}{r} 8\cancel{6}6^{16} \\ -27 \\ \hline 59 \end{array}$$

9.
$$\begin{array}{r} 7\cancel{3}3^{13} \\ -25 \\ \hline 48 \end{array}$$

10.
$$\begin{array}{r} 3\cancel{2}2^{12} \\ -18 \\ \hline 14 \end{array}$$

11.
$$\begin{array}{r} 4\cancel{5}5^{15} \\ -36 \\ \hline 9 \end{array}$$

12.
$$\begin{array}{r} \cancel{7}7^{17} \\ -39 \\ \hline 38 \end{array}$$

11

Pet Stories

Read the sentences and answer the questions. Show your work.

1. On Saturday, 14 people came to visit the pet shop.
   On Sunday, 25 people visited the shop. How many people visited
   the pet shop altogether? _____

2. Paul, the pet shop owner, had 38 goldfish in his pet shop. People
   bought 27 of the goldfish and took them home. How many
   goldfish are left in the pet shop? _____

3. There are 55 cages in all in the pet shop. Paul keeps 38 cages in
   the front of the store to show the animals. He keeps the rest of the
   cages in the back of the store. How many cages are in the back of
   the store? _____

Tic-Tac-Toe

Find the place value of 4 in each number.

Follow the code and mark each square with an X or an O.

Circle the winning row.

Ones place – X
Tens place – O
Hundreds place – X
Thousands place – O

34	545	84
439	4635	40
2348	846	5421

3264	348	4306
42	14	2047
4219	84	409

Doggy Bones

Compare each set of numbers. Write in the <, >, or = sign.

1. 435 < 453

2. 399 < 401

3. 3278 < 4899

4. 603 > 588

5. 2987 > 2897

6. 658 < 688

7. 5629 < 5962

8. 7453 = 7453

9. 556 < 656

10. 3636 < 6363

11. 1199 > 1275

12. 935 = 935

Cat Count

Round each number to the nearest ten or hundred.
Write the number on the line.

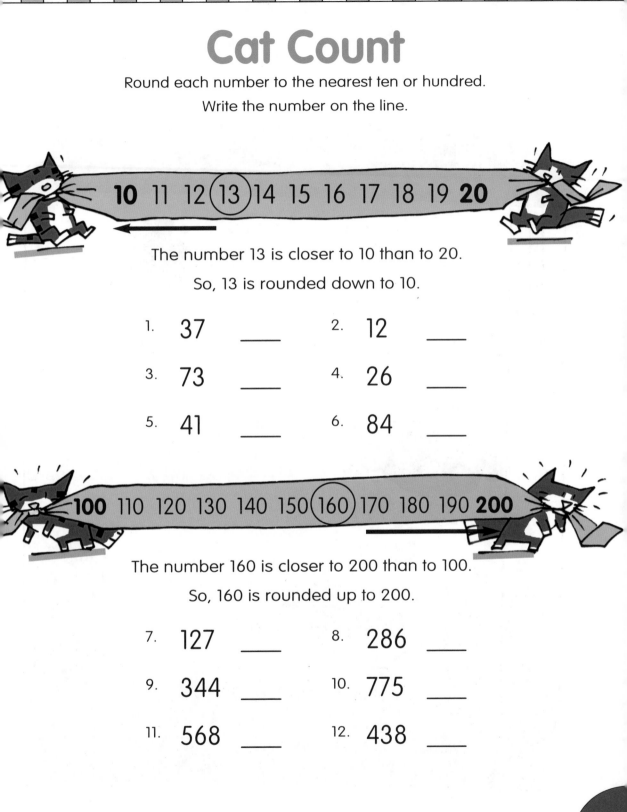

10 11 12 (13) 14 15 16 17 18 19 20

The number 13 is closer to 10 than to 20.

So, 13 is rounded down to 10.

1. 37 ___   2. 12 ___

3. 73 ___   4. 26 ___

5. 41 ___   6. 84 ___

100 110 120 130 140 150 (160) 170 180 190 200

The number 160 is closer to 200 than to 100.

So, 160 is rounded up to 200.

7. 127 ___   8. 286 ___

9. 344 ___   10. 775 ___

11. 568 ___   12. 438 ___

Turtle Tank

Add the numbers and write the sums.

1. 435
  +223

2. 347
  +451

3. 725
  +162

4. 814
  +120

5. 473
  +412

6. 165
  +801

7. 1435
  +2142

8. 5323
  +2411

9. 2705
  +6032

10. 7820
  +2137

11. 1332
  +8406

12. 3390
  +2507

Subtraction Snake

Subtract and regroup to solve each problem.

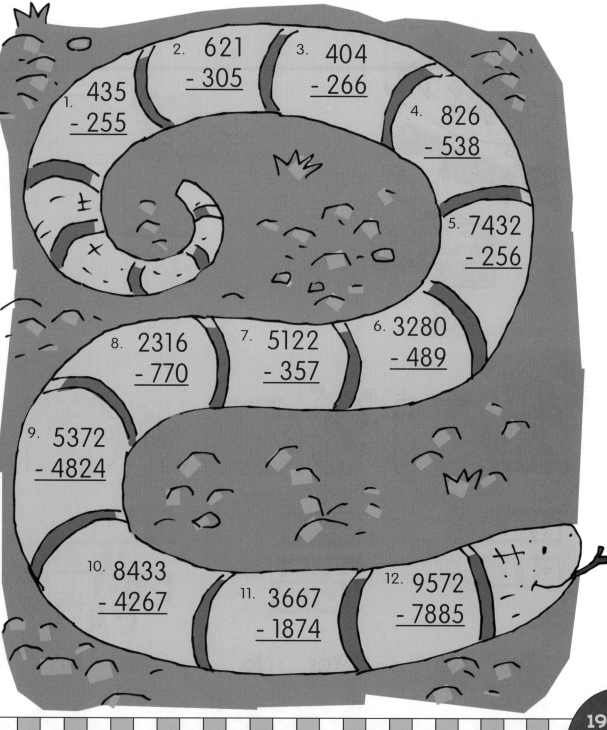

1. 435
   − 255

2. 621
   − 305

3. 404
   − 266

4. 826
   − 538

5. 7432
   − 256

6. 3280
   − 489

7. 5122
   − 357

8. 2316
   − 770

9. 5372
   − 4824

10. 8433
    − 4267

11. 3667
    − 1874

12. 9572
    − 7885

Pet Prices

Annie has $30.00 to buy a pet. Count the bills and coins by each pet and write the price on the tag. Can Annie buy the pet? Circle **Yes** or **No**.

1. **Yes   No**

2. **Yes   No**   3. **Yes   No**   4. **Yes   No**

Pet Purchases

Look at the price for each item and solve the problems.

$ 5.25

$ 3.38

$ 4.40

$ 2.75

$ 6.99

1. Jake bought
   He paid $5.00.
   His change was $____.____ ____

2. Sara bought   and
   She spent $____.____ ____ in all.

3. Kevin bought
   He paid $10.00.
   His change was $____.____ ____

4. Bonnie wants to buy
   She only has $4.00.
   She needs $____.____ ____ more.

5. John bought   and
   He paid $10.00.
   His change was $____.____ ____

6. Rachel bought
   She paid $5.00.
   Her change was $____.____ ____

21

Pets for Sale!

The chart shows how many of each kind of pet were sold each day.
Use the chart to answer the questions below.

Monday	
Tuesday	
Wednesday	
Thursday	
Friday	

1. What was the highest number of cats sold in one day? _____

2. How many birds were sold in all five days? _____

3. On which day were the most birds sold? _____

4. On which day were no cats sold? _____

5. What was the highest number of fish sold in one day? _____

6. On which day were the fewest animals sold? _____

Favorite Pets

The pet shop owner had people vote for their favorite pets.
Use the graph to answer the questions below.

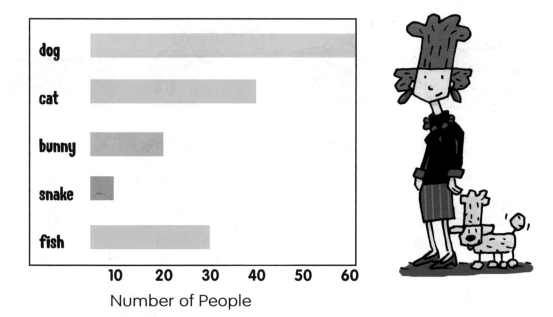

Number of People

1. How many people chose snakes as their favorite pet? __10__

2. How many more people voted for cats than snakes? __40__

3. Which pet received the most number of votes? __dog__

4. How many more votes does the snake need in order for it to
   have the same number of votes as the fish? __2 More__

5. If each person cast only one vote,
   how many people voted altogether? __60__

Daily Pet Plans

Write the hands on the clocks to show the correct times.

1. Puppies wake up
8:00

2. Puppies eat
12:15

3. Puppies play
2:00

4. Puppies sleep
3:00

5. The kittens wake up 2 hours later than the puppies.

6. The snakes eat 3 hours earlier than the puppies.

7. The hamsters play 1 and a half hours later than the puppies.

8. The bunnies go to sleep 15 minutes after the puppies.

Feeding Time

Look at the clocks and figure out how much time
it takes to feed each animal.

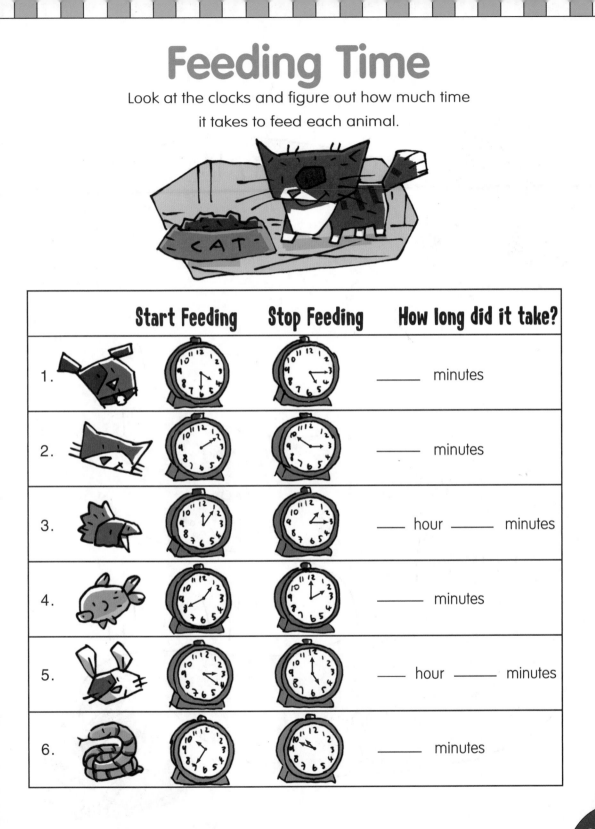

		Start Feeding	Stop Feeding	How long did it take?
1.				_____ minutes
2.				_____ minutes
3.				___ hour ___ minutes
4.				_____ minutes
5.				___ hour ___ minutes
6.				_____ minutes

1/9/14

Leash Lesson

Look at each set of numbers.

Fill in the missing number in the sequence.

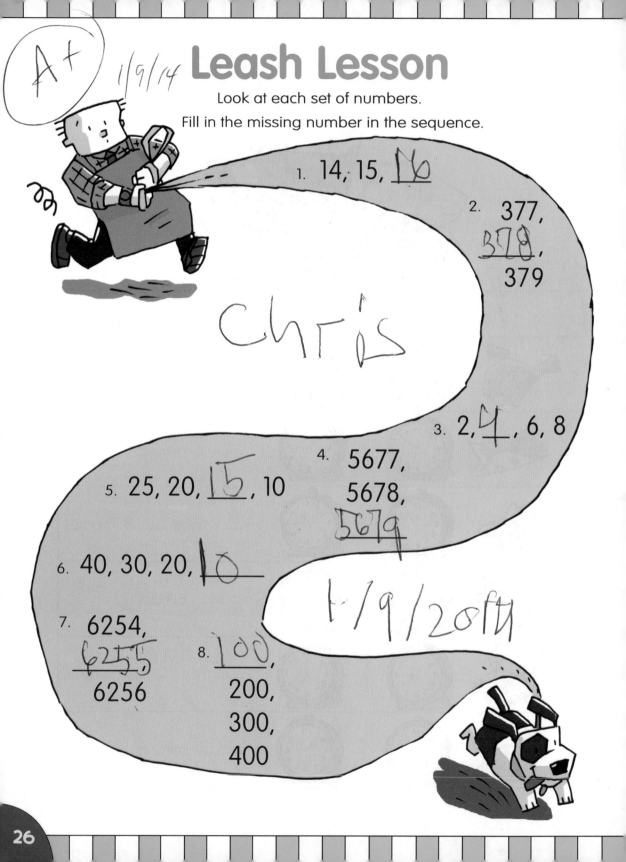

1. 14, 15, 16

2. 377, 378, 379

Chris

3. 2, 4, 6, 8

4. 5677, 5678, 5679

5. 25, 20, 15, 10

6. 40, 30, 20, 10

1/9/2014

7. 6254, 6255, 6256

8. 100, 200, 300, 400

Pets on Parade

Look at the order of the pets in the parade.
Read each statement and circle **True** or **False**.

Chris 1/9, Excellent 2014 1/9/14

1. The bird is the first animal in line.   **True** (**False**)

2. The hamster is the fourth animal in line. (**True**) **False**

3. The cat and the snake are next to each other.   **True** (**False**)

4. The snake is the last animal in line. (**True**) **False**

5. The bird is the third animal in line. (**True**) **False**

6. There are three animals between the dog and the snake.
(**True**) **False**

Shapes at Play

Count how many of each shape is in the picture. Fill in the chart.

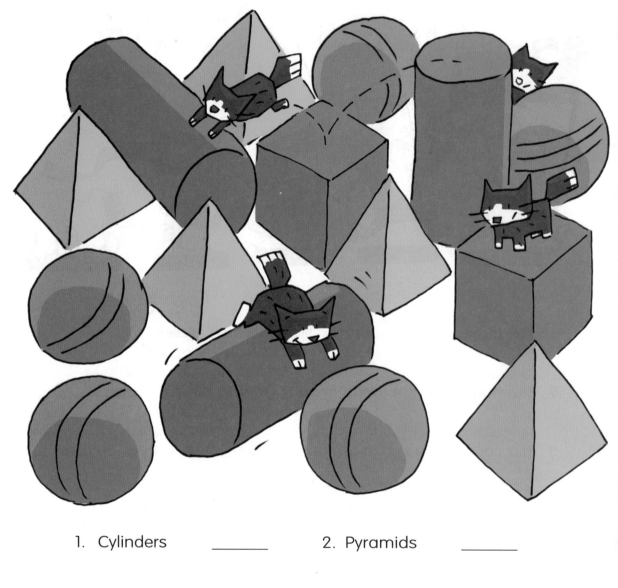

1. Cylinders _____   2. Pyramids _____

3. Cubes _____   4. Spheres _____

Fraction Action

Write a fraction to show how many parts are shaded in each shape.

Count how many total parts.
Write the number below the line.

Count how many shaded parts.
Write the number above the line.

$$\frac{3}{4}$$

1. _____
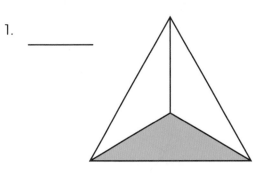

2. _____
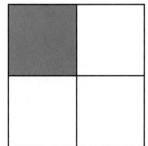

3. _____
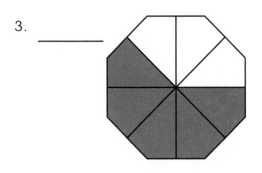

4. _____
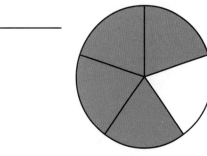

Shady Shapes

Shade the parts inside the shape to equal the fraction.

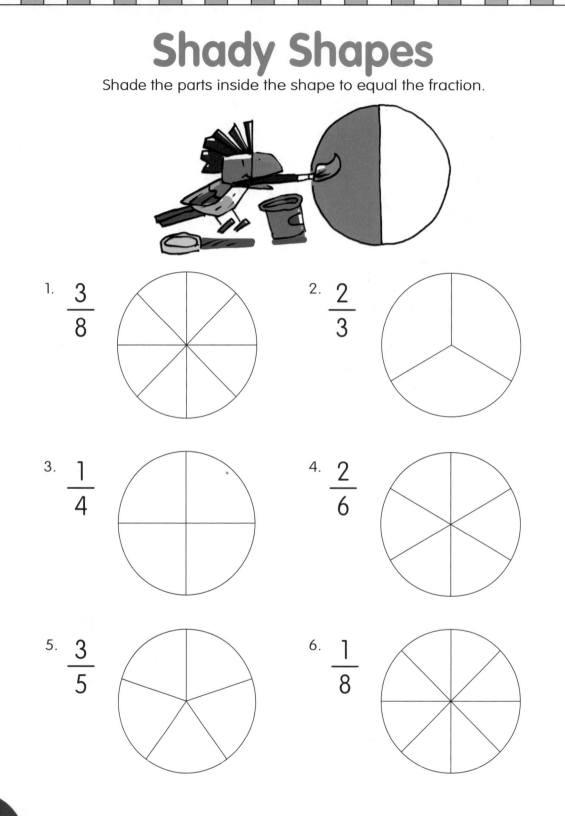

1. $\dfrac{3}{8}$

2. $\dfrac{2}{3}$

3. $\dfrac{1}{4}$

4. $\dfrac{2}{6}$

5. $\dfrac{3}{5}$

6. $\dfrac{1}{8}$

Fraction Frogs

Look at the picture. Draw a line from each question to the fraction that answers it.

1. What fraction of the frogs are swimming?

$$\frac{1}{7}$$

2. What fraction of the frogs are eating?

$$\frac{2}{7}$$

3. What fraction of the frogs are on a rock?

$$\frac{3}{7}$$

4. What fraction of the frogs are not in the water?

$$\frac{4}{7}$$

Pets in Nets

Look at each picture. Write the fraction that shows
how many animals are inside each net.

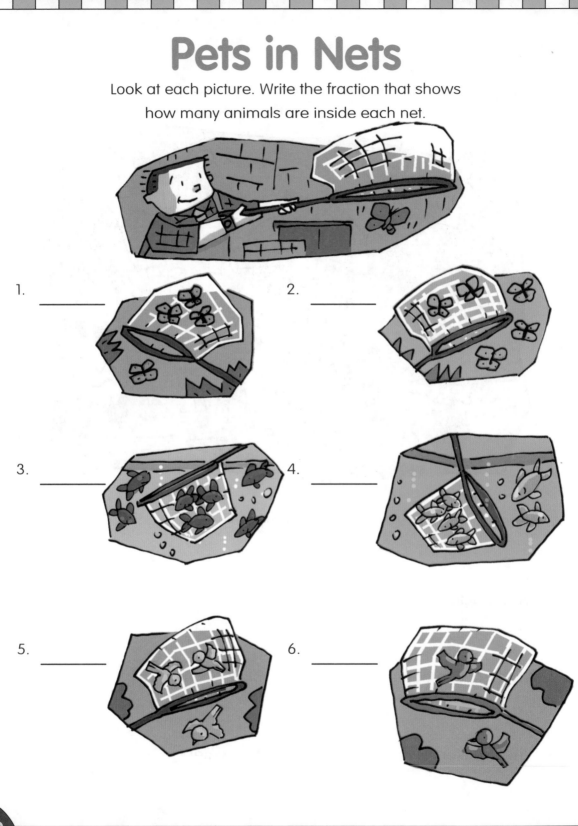

1. _____

2. _____

3. _____

4. _____

5. _____

6. _____

Hamster Halftime

Look at each set of shapes and write the fractions.

 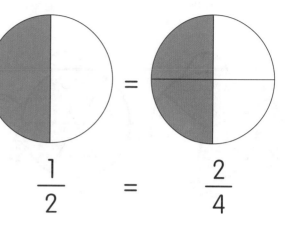

$$\frac{1}{2} = \frac{2}{4}$$

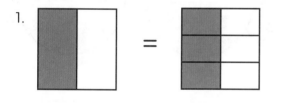

1. _____ = _____

2. _____ = _____

 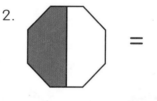

3. _____ = _____

4. _____ = _____

Fish Fractions

Count the shaded parts and write the fraction.

If the two fractions are equivalent, write =. If not, write ≠.

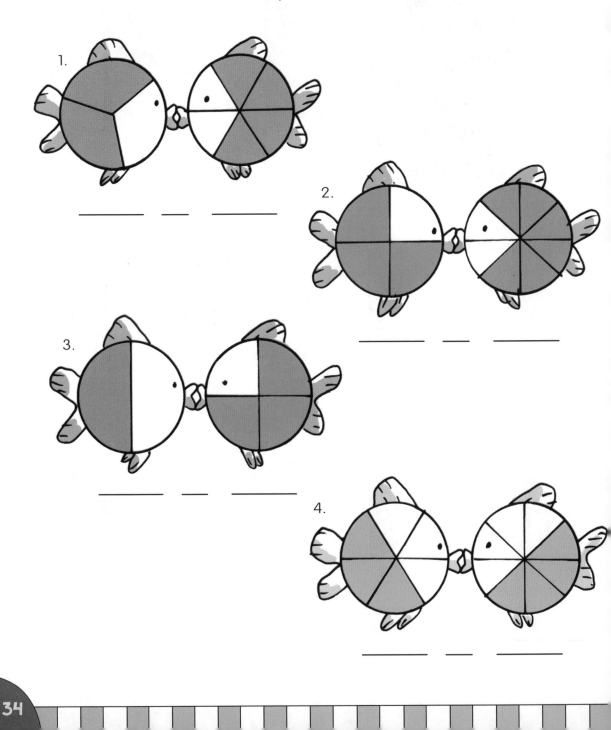

1. _____ ___ _____

2. _____ ___ _____

3. _____ ___ _____

4. _____ ___ _____

Fraction Fun

Read the sentences and write the fraction to answer the question.

1. There were 6 bunnies in the cage. In the afternoon, 5 of them fell asleep. What fraction of the bunnies were sleeping? _____

2. Paul had 5 goldfish in the tank. He fed 3 of the fish. What fraction of the fish did Paul feed? _____

3. There were 3 cats in the pet store. Paul gave 1 of them a bath. What fraction of the cats took a bath? _____

4. In the pet shop window there were 10 dogs. Paul put collars on 5 of the dogs. What fraction of the dogs wore collars? _____

Pets on the Loose!

You can find the location of something by using number pairs.

The first number shows how many spaces to the right.

The second number shows how many spaces up.

Write the number pair that shows the location of each animal.

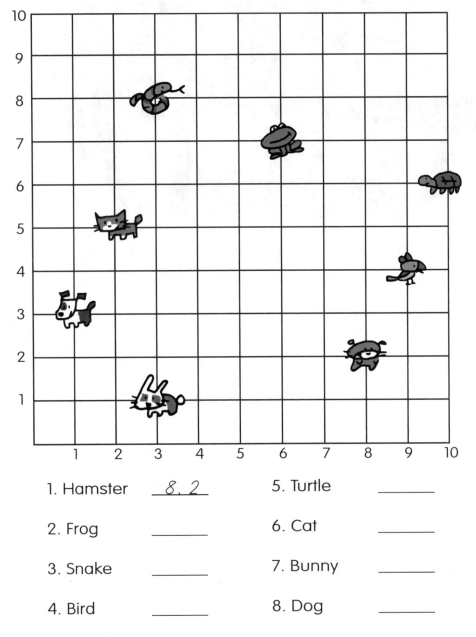

1. Hamster _8, 2_   5. Turtle _____

2. Frog _____   6. Cat _____

3. Snake _____   7. Bunny _____

4. Bird _____   8. Dog _____

Multiplying Mice

Multiply. If the answer is even, write X below the problem.
If the answer is odd, write O. Which mouse wins the game of tic-tac-toe?

8 x 5 = __	3 x 5 = ___	2 x 6 = ___
3 x 7 = __	7 x 2 = ___	3 x 3 = ___
6 x 4 = ___	5 x 7 = ___	5 x 5 = ___

Frog Fives

Multiply. Write the answer inside the lily pad.

1. 3 x 5 = ___

2. 2 x 5 = ___

3. 8 x 5 = ___

4. 6 x 5 = ___

6. 10 x 5 = ___

5. 1 x 5 = ___

7. 9 x 5 = ___

8. 7 x 5 = ___

Puppy Surprise

Multiply. Use the letter next to each answer to help break the code.

1. 10
    x 4
    E

2. 10
    x 8
    N

3. 10
    x 6
    I

4. 10
    x 2
    G

5. 10
    x 9
    O

6. 10
    x 1
    G

4. 10
    x 7
    O

5. 10
    x 5
    T

6. 10
    x 3
    D

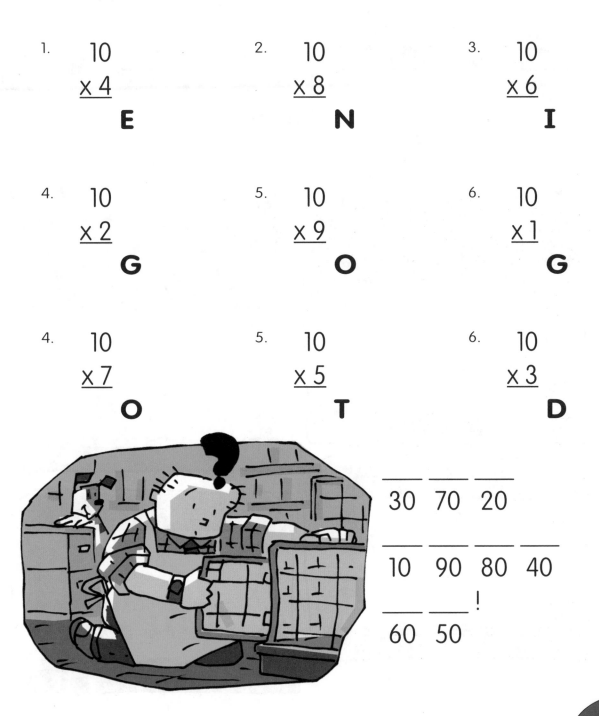

__ __ __
30 70 20

__ __ __ __
10 90 80 40
            !
__ __
60 50

Tanks of Tables

Multiply to complete each table. Find each answer and
write the letter to answer the question.

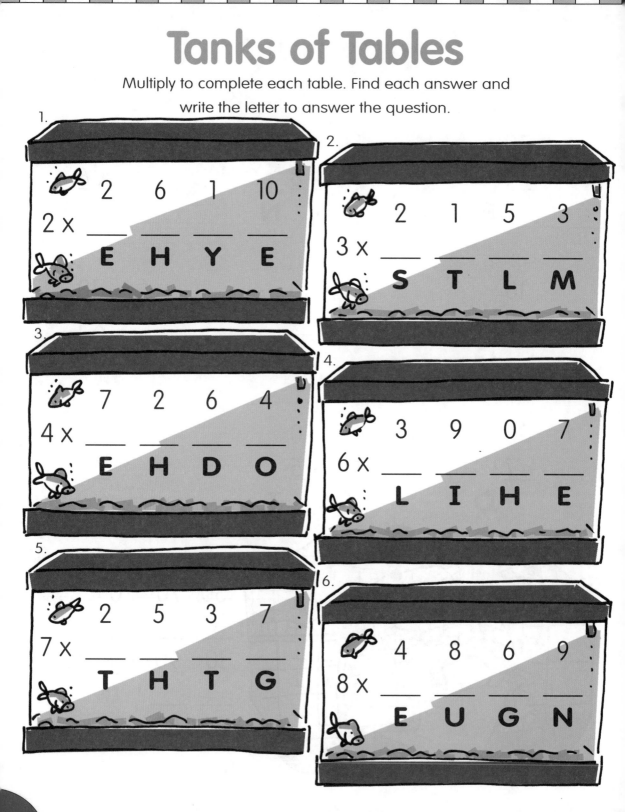

1.

	2	6	1	10
2 ×	___	___	___	___
	E	H	Y	E

2.

	2	1	5	3
3 ×	___	___	___	___
	S	T	L	M

3.

	7	2	6	4
4 ×	___	___	___	___
	E	H	D	O

4.

	3	9	0	7
6 ×	___	___	___	___
	L	I	H	E

5.

	2	5	3	7
7 ×	___	___	___	___
	T	H	T	G

6.

	4	8	6	9
8 ×	___	___	___	___
	E	U	G	N

7.

9 × 5 4 7 3

H S F E

8.

11 × 6 2 8 9

O I M S

Why did the detective jump into the aquarium?

___ ___   ___ ___ ___ ___ ___ ___ ___
12 4   3   8 66 64 48   0 21

___ ___   ___ ___ ___ ___ ___ ___ ___
35 27   36 88 42 15 18 28 24

___ ___ ___ ___ ___ ___ ___ ___ ___
99 16   9 32 14 45 22 72 49

___ ___ ___ ___ ___
63 54   6 12   2

Spot the Dog

Multiply.

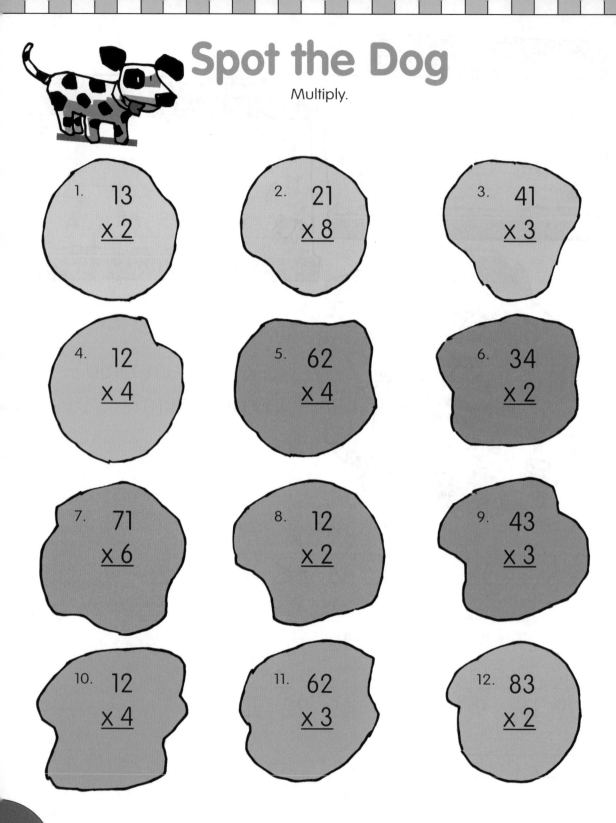

1. 13
   x 2

2. 21
   x 8

3. 41
   x 3

4. 12
   x 4

5. 62
   x 4

6. 34
   x 2

7. 71
   x 6

8. 12
   x 2

9. 43
   x 3

10. 12
    x 4

11. 62
    x 3

12. 83
    x 2

Bath Time!

Multiply.

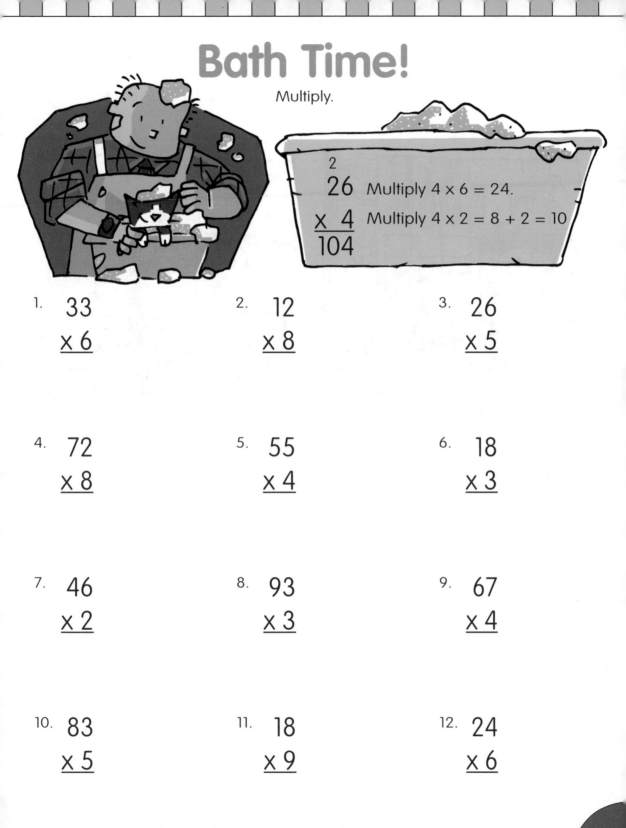

$$
\begin{array}{r}
{}^{2} \\
26 \\
\times\ 4 \\
\hline
104
\end{array}
$$

Multiply 4 x 6 = 24.

Multiply 4 x 2 = 8 + 2 = 10

1.
$$
\begin{array}{r}
33 \\
\times\ 6 \\
\hline
\end{array}
$$

2.
$$
\begin{array}{r}
12 \\
\times\ 8 \\
\hline
\end{array}
$$

3.
$$
\begin{array}{r}
26 \\
\times\ 5 \\
\hline
\end{array}
$$

4.
$$
\begin{array}{r}
72 \\
\times\ 8 \\
\hline
\end{array}
$$

5.
$$
\begin{array}{r}
55 \\
\times\ 4 \\
\hline
\end{array}
$$

6.
$$
\begin{array}{r}
18 \\
\times\ 3 \\
\hline
\end{array}
$$

7.
$$
\begin{array}{r}
46 \\
\times\ 2 \\
\hline
\end{array}
$$

8.
$$
\begin{array}{r}
93 \\
\times\ 3 \\
\hline
\end{array}
$$

9.
$$
\begin{array}{r}
67 \\
\times\ 4 \\
\hline
\end{array}
$$

10.
$$
\begin{array}{r}
83 \\
\times\ 5 \\
\hline
\end{array}
$$

11.
$$
\begin{array}{r}
18 \\
\times\ 9 \\
\hline
\end{array}
$$

12.
$$
\begin{array}{r}
24 \\
\times\ 6 \\
\hline
\end{array}
$$

Copy Cats

Read the sentences and solve the problems. Show your work.

1. There are 6 cats at the pet store. Each pet has 8 whiskers.
    How many whiskers do the cats have altogether?

    _____

2. Paul, the pet shop owner, has 3 windows for displaying animals.
    He put 4 cats in each window.
    How many cats are in all the windows? _____

3. The pet shop sold cats for 12 days. Each day 8 cats were sold.
    How many cats were sold overall? _____

4. On Friday there were 7 cats in the pet shop.
    Each cat meowed 35 times.
    How many meows did the cats make in all? _____

Puppy Chow

Divide.

1. 12 ÷ 4 = _____

2. 10 ÷ 5 = _____

3. 14 ÷ 7 = _____

4. 24 ÷ 6 = _____

5. 55 ÷ 5 = _____

6. 15 ÷ 3 = _____

7. 35 ÷ 7 = _____

8. 8 ÷ 2 = _____

9. 49 ÷ 7 = _____

Division Tables

Divide to complete each table.

÷ 2

14	7
12	6
22	11
16	8

÷ 5

25	___
30	___
15	___
45	___

÷ 6

18	___
36	___
42	___
24	___

÷ 9

27	___
54	___
36	___
18	___

	÷ 4
16	___
20	___
12	___
32	___

	÷ 3
18	___
33	___
15	___
9	___

	÷ 7
21	___
56	___
49	___
35	___

	÷ 8
64	___
16	___
40	___
32	___

A Pair of Pups

Divide and show your work. Use the letter next to each answer to help solve the code.

$$\begin{array}{r} 47 \\ 3\overline{)141} \\ -12 \\ \hline 21 \end{array}$$

1. $4\overline{)48}$ **P**

2. $5\overline{)175}$ **U**

3. $3\overline{)132}$ **I**

4. $8\overline{)112}$ **E**

5. $4\overline{)252}$ **L**

6. $7\overline{)133}$ **S**

7. $6\overline{)168}$ **O**

8. $2\overline{)190}$ **P**

9. $4\overline{)232}$ **V**

10. $8\overline{)392}$ **T**

11. $6\overline{)462}$ **P**

12. $3\overline{)246}$ **Y**

$$\overline{44} \; \overline{49} \; \overset{,}{\overline{19}}$$

$$\overline{12} \; \overline{35} \; \overline{95} \; \overline{77} \; \overline{82}$$

$$\overline{63} \; \overline{28} \; \overline{58} \; \overline{14}$$

Pet Shop Window

Divide and show your work.

1.
$6\overline{)246}$

2.
$4\overline{)352}$

3.
$5\overline{)320}$

4.
$9\overline{)459}$

5.
$2\overline{)94}$

6.
$3\overline{)114}$

7.
$4\overline{)364}$

8.
$7\overline{)133}$

9.
$8\overline{)232}$

10.
$2\overline{)146}$

11.
$9\overline{)315}$

12.
$8\overline{)440}$

The Long Leash

Divide and show your work. Write the remainder for each problem.

$$\begin{array}{r} 39 \text{ R1} \\ 2\overline{)79} \\ -6 \\ \hline 19 \\ -18 \\ \hline 1 \end{array}$$

1 is the remainder.

1.

$$3\overline{)97}$$

2.

$$8\overline{)137}$$

3.

$$2\overline{)111}$$

4.

$$4\overline{)250}$$

5.

$$6\overline{)92}$$

6.

$$7\overline{)254}$$

7.

$$3\overline{)155}$$

8.

$$5\overline{)148}$$

9.

$$9\overline{)407}$$

10.

$$4\overline{)93}$$

11.

$$2\overline{)147}$$

12.

$$6\overline{)266}$$

Division Dig

Divide and show your work. Write the remainder for each problem.

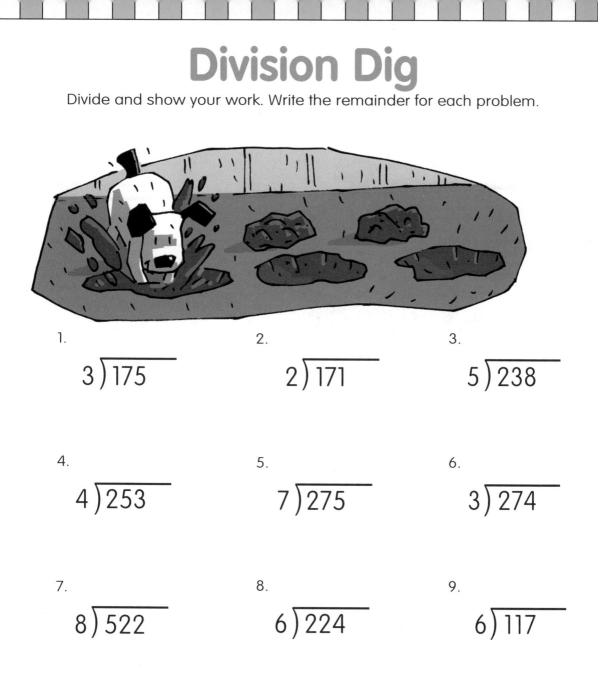

1.

$3\overline{)175}$

2.

$2\overline{)171}$

3.

$5\overline{)238}$

4.

$4\overline{)253}$

5.

$7\overline{)275}$

6.

$3\overline{)274}$

7.

$8\overline{)522}$

8.

$6\overline{)224}$

9.

$6\overline{)117}$

10.

$9\overline{)201}$

11.

$7\overline{)535}$

12.

$8\overline{)394}$

Pet Homes

Read the sentences and solve the problems. Show your work.

1. There are 24 snakes in the pet store. Paul has 6 cages to put them in. If he puts the same number of snakes in each cage, how many snakes will be in each cage? _____

2. Paul has 35 bunnies to keep in the store. He has 11 cages for the bunnies. He can only put 3 bunnies in each cage. How many bunnies will be left over? _____

3. There are 6 fish tanks in the pet shop. Paul has 120 fish to divide equally among the tanks. How many fish can he put in each tank? _____

4. There are 4 windows for displaying pets at the pet shop. Paul has 26 kittens to put in the windows. He wants to put the same number of kittens in each window. What is the greatest number of kittens he can put in each window? _____ How many kittens will be left over? _____

Reptile Review

Solve the problems.

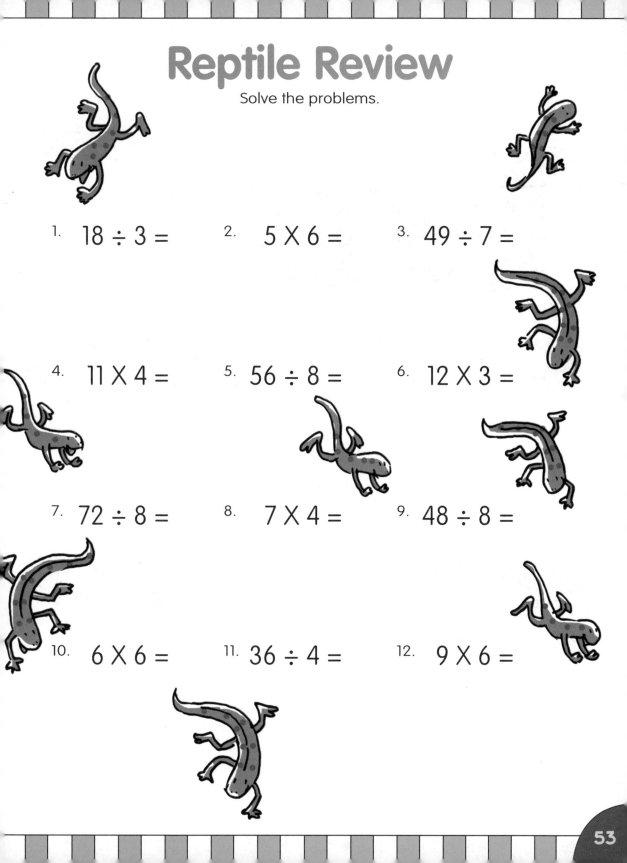

1. $18 \div 3 =$ 2. $5 \times 6 =$ 3. $49 \div 7 =$

4. $11 \times 4 =$ 5. $56 \div 8 =$ 6. $12 \times 3 =$

7. $72 \div 8 =$ 8. $7 \times 4 =$ 9. $48 \div 8 =$

10. $6 \times 6 =$ 11. $36 \div 4 =$ 12. $9 \times 6 =$

Furry Fact Families

Use the numbers inside each paw print to fill in the fact family problems.

4 • 5 • 20

$$5 \times 4 = 20$$
$$4 \times 5 = 20$$
$$20 \div 5 = 4$$
$$20 \div 4 = 5$$

2 • 7 • 14

1.
___ X ___ = ___
___ X ___ = ___
___ ÷ ___ = ___
___ ÷ ___ = ___

8 • 6 • 48

2.
___ X ___ = ___
___ X ___ = ___
___ ÷ ___ = ___
___ ÷ ___ = ___

3 • 5 • 15

3.
___ X ___ = ___
___ X ___ = ___
___ ÷ ___ = ___
___ ÷ ___ = ___

4 • 9 • 36

4.
___ X ___ = ___
___ X ___ = ___
___ ÷ ___ = ___
___ ÷ ___ = ___

More Furry Fact Families

Use the numbers inside each paw print to fill in the fact family problems.

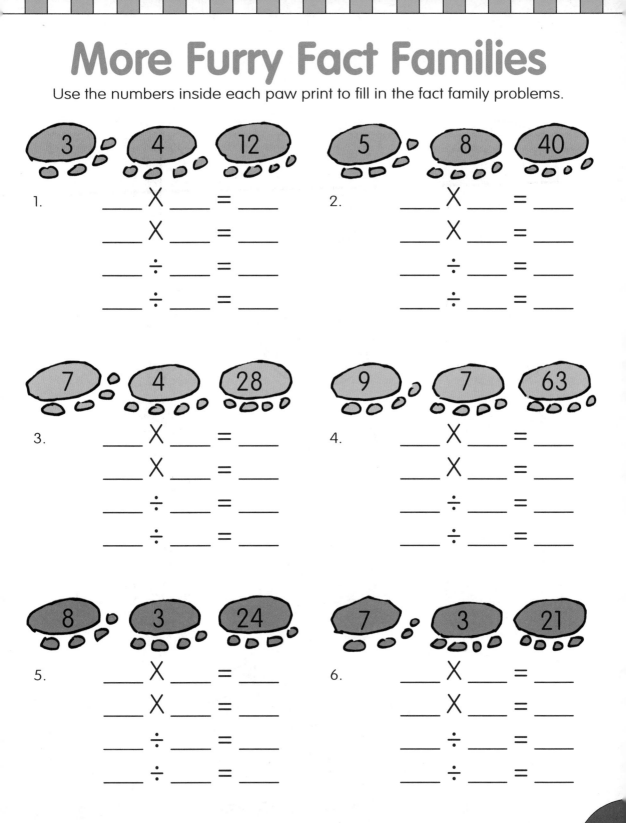

3 4 12

1.   ___ X ___ = ___
     ___ X ___ = ___
     ___ ÷ ___ = ___
     ___ ÷ ___ = ___

5 8 40

2.   ___ X ___ = ___
     ___ X ___ = ___
     ___ ÷ ___ = ___
     ___ ÷ ___ = ___

7 4 28

3.   ___ X ___ = ___
     ___ X ___ = ___
     ___ ÷ ___ = ___
     ___ ÷ ___ = ___

9 7 63

4.   ___ X ___ = ___
     ___ X ___ = ___
     ___ ÷ ___ = ___
     ___ ÷ ___ = ___

8 3 24

5.   ___ X ___ = ___
     ___ X ___ = ___
     ___ ÷ ___ = ___
     ___ ÷ ___ = ___

7 3 21

6.   ___ X ___ = ___
     ___ X ___ = ___
     ___ ÷ ___ = ___
     ___ ÷ ___ = ___

Bouncing Balls

Multiply or divide to solve the problems.

1. 23×3

2. $4 \overline{)168}$

3. 14×2

4. $5 \overline{)405}$

5. 43×3

6. $6 \overline{)366}$

7. 45×4

8. $7 \overline{)217}$

9. 38×6

10. $3 \overline{)99}$

11. 27×5

12. $8 \overline{)568}$

Missing Mice

Fill in the missing number
for each problem.

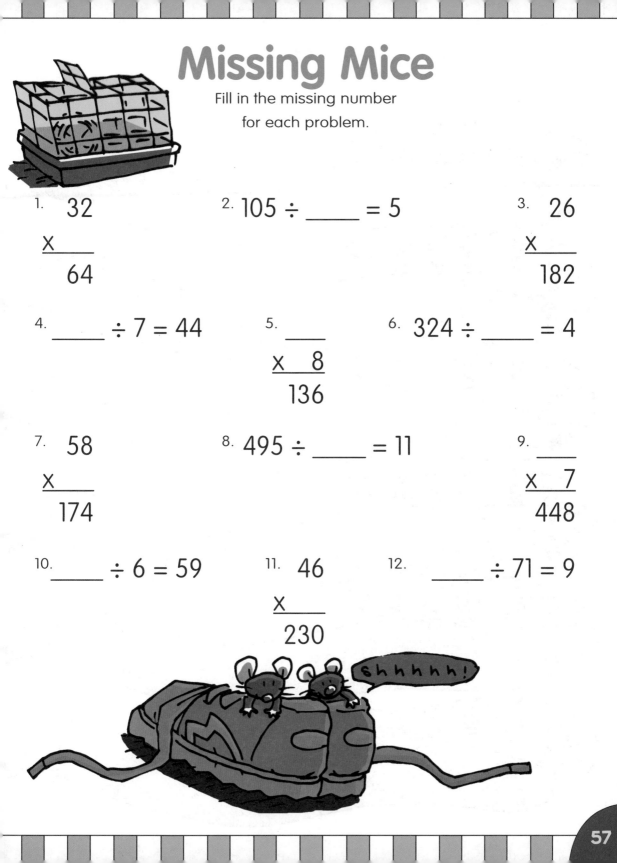

1.
$$\begin{array}{r} 32 \\ \times \underline{} \\ 64 \end{array}$$

2. $105 \div \underline{} = 5$

3.
$$\begin{array}{r} 26 \\ \times \underline{} \\ 182 \end{array}$$

4. $\underline{} \div 7 = 44$

5.
$$\begin{array}{r} \underline{} \\ \times 8 \\ \hline 136 \end{array}$$

6. $324 \div \underline{} = 4$

7.
$$\begin{array}{r} 58 \\ \times \underline{} \\ 174 \end{array}$$

8. $495 \div \underline{} = 11$

9.
$$\begin{array}{r} \underline{} \\ \times 7 \\ \hline 448 \end{array}$$

10. $\underline{} \div 6 = 59$

11.
$$\begin{array}{r} 46 \\ \times \underline{} \\ 230 \end{array}$$

12. $\underline{} \div 71 = 9$

Snake Surprise

Fill in the missing numbers and solve the problems.

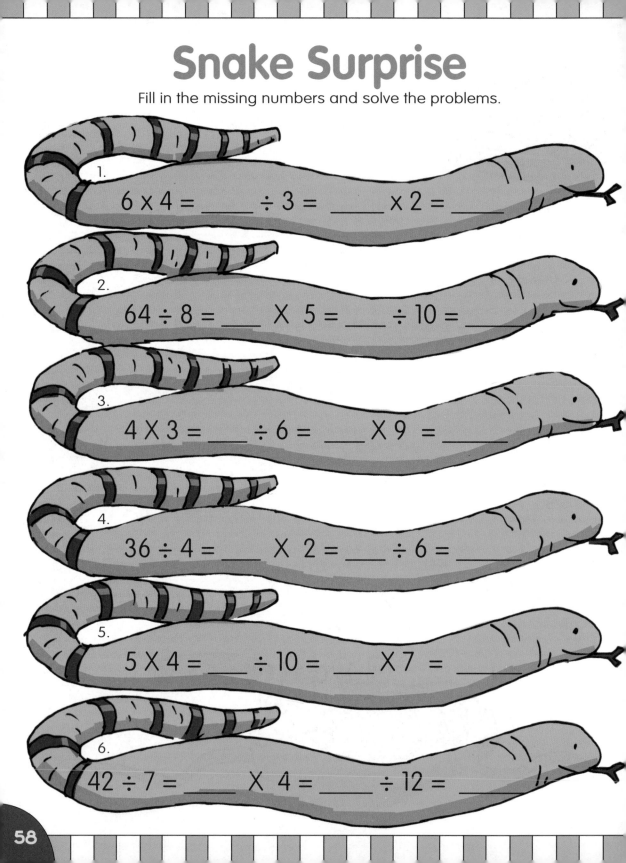

1. $6 \times 4 = \underline{} \div 3 = \underline{} \times 2 = \underline{}$

2. $64 \div 8 = \underline{} \times 5 = \underline{} \div 10 = \underline{}$

3. $4 \times 3 = \underline{} \div 6 = \underline{} \times 9 = \underline{}$

4. $36 \div 4 = \underline{} \times 2 = \underline{} \div 6 = \underline{}$

5. $5 \times 4 = \underline{} \div 10 = \underline{} \times 7 = \underline{}$

6. $42 \div 7 = \underline{} \times 4 = \underline{} \div 12 = \underline{}$

Pet Path

Multiply or divide.
Help the pets find their way back to the cage.
Color all the boxes whose problems
have a remainder.

1. $4\overline{)315}$	2. $8\overline{)568}$	3. $\begin{array}{r} 43 \\ \times\ 5 \\ \hline \end{array}$
4. $5\overline{)286}$	5. $8\overline{)250}$	6. $\begin{array}{r} 54 \\ \times\ 6 \\ \hline \end{array}$
7. $\begin{array}{r} 62 \\ \times\ 3 \\ \hline \end{array}$	8. $3\overline{)115}$	9. $\begin{array}{r} 31 \\ \times\ 9 \\ \hline \end{array}$
10. $7\overline{)462}$	11. $\begin{array}{r} 19 \\ \times\ 8 \\ \hline \end{array}$	12. $4\overline{)217}$

Pet Parts

Paul counts all his pets before he closes the shop.

Read the sentences and solve the problems.

1. Paul counted 37 puppies in the pet shop.

    Each puppy has 2 ears.

    How many puppy ears are there in all? _____

2. Paul counted 114 whiskers total on all his bunnies.

    Each bunny has 6 whiskers.

    How many bunnies are there? _____

3. Paul counted 116 legs on all his cats. Each cat has 4 legs.

    How many cats are in his store? _____

4. There are 12 bird cages in the pet store.

    Paul counted 9 feathers in the bottom of each cage.

    How many feathers are there in all? _____

Closing Time

Paul, the pet shop owner, is putting everything away for the night.
Read the sentences and solve the problems.

1. There are 48 cans of fish food to go back on the shelves. Each shelf can hold 12 cans of food. How many shelves will he need to use to put all the cans away? _____

2. Paul needs to wash all of the pet bowls. There are 29 pets in the shop who eat from bowls. Each pet has 2 bowls, one for food and one for water. How many bowls does Paul need to wash in all? _____

3. The bunnies need to go back into their cages. Paul has 52 bunnies. Each cage must hold 3 bunnies. How many cages does he need? How many bunnies are left over?

_____

4. Paul needs to count all of the fish. He has 27 fish tanks. There are 9 fish in each tank. How many fish does Paul have in all? _____

Page 4
1. 12
2. 11
3. 17
4. 18
5. 36
6. 57
7. 98
8. 37
9. 49
10. 88

Page 5
1. 2
2. 4
3. 1
4. 3
5. 11
6. 21
7. 13
8. 32
9. 25
10. 23
11. 71
12. 22
PURRFECT PALS

Page 6
    + 4
4   8
7   11
5   9
6   10;
    + 6
3   9
9   15
1   7
2   8;
    +8
8   16
5   13
9   17
3   11

Page 7
14   8   6
10   5   5
4   3   1;
26   11   15
14   8   6
12   3   9;
45   30   15
36   24   12
9   6   3;
32   12   20
21   8   13
11   4   7

Page 8
    12
(6 + 6)
(7 + 5)
(8 + 4)
9 + 2
    9
(3 + 6)
(4 + 5)
8 + 2
(2 + 7)

    8
(10 - 2)
11 - 4
(17 - 9)
(14 - 6)
    6
15 - 7
(12 - 6)
(14 - 8)
(10 - 4)

Page 9
6 + 9 = 15
9 + 6 = 15
15 - 6 = 9
15 - 9 = 6;
8 + 4 = 12
4 + 8 = 12
12 - 8 = 4
12 - 4 = 8;
6 + 12 = 18
12 + 6 = 18
18 - 6 = 12
18 - 12 = 6;
7 + 8 = 15
8 + 7 = 15
15 - 8 = 7
15 - 7 = 8

Page 10
1. 22
2. 23
3. 32
4. 61
5. 51
6. 40
7. 41
8. 82
9. 92
10. 83
11. 90
12. 91

Page 11
1. 17
2. 36
3. 7
4. 58
5. 44
6. 28
7. 18
8. 59
9. 48
10. 14
11. 9
12. 38

Page 12
1. 14 + 25 = 39 people
2. 38 - 27 = 11 goldfish
3. 55 - 38 = 17   cages

Page 13

X	O	X
X	O	X
O	O	X

X	O	O
O	X	O
O	X	X

Page 14
1. 435 < 453
2. 399 < 401
3. 3278 < 4899
4. 603 > 588
5. 2987 > 2897
6. 658 < 688
7. 5629 < 5962
8. 7453 = 7453
9. 556 < 656
10. 3636 < 6363
11. 1199 < 1275
12. 935 = 935

Page 15
1. 40
2. 10
3. 70
4. 30
5. 40
6. 80
7. 100
8. 300
9. 300
10. 800
11. 600
12. 800

Page 16
1. 658
2. 798
3. 887
4. 934
5. 885
6. 966
7. 3577
8. 7734
9. 8737
10. 9957
11. 9738
12. 5897

Page 17
1. 101
2. 133
3. 125
4. 43
5. 352
6. 531
7. 1523
8. 2341
9. 2202
10. 4305
11. 425
SWIM in SCHOOLS

Page 18
1. 672 (shaded)
2. 811
3. 727
4. 835
5. 5160 (shaded)
6. 3024 (shaded)
7. 8524 (shaded)
8. 2293
9. 8721
10. 9129
11. 9216 (shaded)
12. 9162 (shaded)

Page 19
1. 180
2. 316
3. 138
4. 288
5. 7176
6. 2791
7. 4765
8. 1546
9. 548
10. 4166
11. 1793
12. 1687

Page 20
1. $ 25.50, Yes
2. $ 30.45, No
3. $ 7.05, Yes
4. $ 17.00, Yes

Page 21
1. $ 1.62
2. $ 7.15
3. $ 3.01
4. $ 1.25
5. $ 1.37
6. $ .60

Page 22
1. 3
2. 9
3. Tuesday
4. Friday
5. 4
6. Wednesday

Page 23
1. 10
2. 30
3. dog
4. 20
5. 160

Page 24
1.
2.
3.
4.
5.
6.
7.
8.

Page 25
1. 45 minutes
2. 40 minutes
3. 1 hour 10 minutes
4. 20 minutes
5. 1 hour 40 minutes
6. 15 minutes

Page 26
1. 16
2. 378
3. 4
4. 5679
5. 15
6. 10
7. 6255
8. 100

Page 27
1. False
2. True
3. False
4. True
5. True
6. True

Page 28
1. 3
2. 5
3. 2
4. 5

Page 29
1. 1/3
2. 1/4
3. 5/8
4. 4/5

Page 30
1.
2.
3.
4.
5.
6.

Page 31
1. 3/7
2. 1/7
3. 2/7
4. 4/7

Page 32
1. 3/4
2. 2/5
3. 3/7
4. 4/6
5. 2/3
6. 1/2

Page 33
1. 1/2 = 3/6
2. 1/2 = 4/8
3. 1/2 = 5/10
4. 1/2 = 6/12

Page 34
1. 2/3 = 4/6
2. 3/4 = 6/8
3. 1/2 ≠ 3/4
4. 3/6 = 4/8

Page 35
1. 5/6
2. 3/5
3. 1/3
4. 5/10 or 1/2

Page 36
1. 8, 2
2. 6,7
3. 3,8
4. 9,4
5. 10,6
6. 2,5
7. 3,1
8. 1,3

Page 37

40 = X	15 = O	12 = X
21 = O	14 = X	9 = O
24 = X	35 = O	25 = O

Page 38
1. 15
2. 10
3. 40
4. 30
5. 5
6. 50
7. 45
8. 35

Page 39
1. 40
2. 80
3. 60
4. 20
5. 90
6. 10
7. 70
8. 50
9. 30
DOG GONE IT

Page 40

	2	6	1	10
2X	4	12	2	20;
	2	1	5	3
3X	6	3	15	9;
	7	2	6	4
4X	28	8	24	16;
	3	6	0	7
6X	18	36	0	42
	2	5	3	7
7X	14	35	21	49;
	4	8	6	9
8X	32	64	48	72;

Page 41

	5	4	7	3
9X	45	36	63	27;
	6	2	8	9
11X	66	22	88	99

HE THOUGHT HE SMELLED SOMETHING FISHY

Page 42
1. 26
2. 168
3. 123
4. 48

5. 248
6. 68
7. 426
8. 24
9. 129
10. 48
11. 186
12. 166

Page 43
1. 198
2. 96
3. 130
4. 576
5. 220
6. 54
7. 92
8. 279
9. 268
10. 415
11. 162
12. 144

Page 44
1. 6 X 8=48 whiskers
2. 3 X 4 = 12 cats
3. 12 X 8 = 96 cats
4. 35 X 7=245 meows

Page 45
1. 3
2. 2
3. 2
4. 4
5. 11
6. 5
7. 5
8. 4
9. 7

Page 46

	÷ 2		÷ 5
14	7	25	5
12	6	30	6
22	11	15	3
16	8	45	9
	÷ 6		÷ 9
18	3	27	3
36	6	54	6
42	7	36	4
24	4	18	2

Page 47

	÷ 4		÷ 3
16	4	18	6
20	5	33	11
12	3	15	5
32	8	9	3
	÷ 7		÷ 8
21	3	64	8
56	8	16	2
49	7	40	5
35	5	32	4

Page 48
1. 12
2. 35
3. 44

4. 14
5. 63
6. 19
7. 28
8. 95
9. 58
10. 49
11. 77
12. 82
IT'S PUPPY LOVE

Page 49
1. 41
2. 88
3. 64
4. 51
5. 47
6. 38
7. 91
8. 19
9. 29
10. 73
11. 35
12. 55

Page 50
R = remainder
1. 32 R1
2. 17 R1
3. 55 R1
4. 62 R2
5. 5 R2
6. 36 R2
7. 51 R2
8. 29 R3
9. 45 R2
10. 23 R1
11. 73 R1
12. 44 R2

Page 51
1. 58 R1
2. 85 R1
3. 47 R3
4. 63 R1
5. 39 R2
6. 91 R1
7. 65 R2
8. 37 R2
9. 19 R3
10. 22 R3
11. 76 R3
12. 49 R2

Page 52
1. 24 ÷ 6 = 4 snakes

2.
```
    11
3 ) 35
    3
    2 remainder
```
2 bunnies left over
3. 120 ÷ 6 = 20 fish per tank

4.
```
    6
4 ) 26
    24
    2
```
6 in each window
2 left over

Page 53
1. 6
2. 30
3. 7
4. 44
5. 7
6. 36
7. 9
8. 28
9. 6
10. 36
11. 9
12. 54

Page 54
1. 2 X 7 = 14
   7 X 2 = 14
   14 ÷ 7 = 2
   14 ÷ 2 = 7
2. 8 X 6 = 48
   6 X 8 = 48
   48 ÷ 8 = 6
   48 ÷ 6 = 8
3. 3 X 5 = 15
   5 X 3 = 15
   15 ÷ 5 = 3
   15 ÷ 3 = 5
4. 4 X 9 = 36
   9 X 4 = 36
   36 ÷ 9 = 4
   36 ÷ 4 = 9

Page 55
1. 3 X 4 = 12
   4 X 3 = 12
   12 ÷ 4 = 3
   12 ÷ 3 = 4
2. 5 X 8 = 40
   8 X 5 = 40
   40 ÷ 8 = 5
   40 ÷ 5 = 8
3. 7 X 4 = 28
   4 X 7 = 28
   28 ÷ 4 = 7
   28 ÷ 7 = 4
4. 9 X 7 = 63
   7 X 9 = 63
   63 ÷ 7 = 9
   63 ÷ 9 = 7
5. 8 X 3 = 24
   3 X 8 = 24
   24 ÷ 3 = 8
   24 ÷ 8 = 3
6. 7 X 3 = 21
   3 X 7 = 21
   21 ÷ 3 = 7
   21 ÷ 7 = 3

Page 56
1. 69
2. 42
3. 28
4. 81
5. 129
6. 61
7. 180
8. 31

9. 228
10. 33
11. 135
12. 71

Page 57
1. 2
2. 21
3. 7
4. 308
5. 17
6. 81
7. 3
8. 45
9. 64
10. 354
11. 5
12. 639

Page 58
1. 6 X 4 = 24 ÷ 3 = 8 X 2 = 16
2. 64 ÷ 8 = 8 X 5 = 40 ÷ 10 = 4
3. 4 X 3 = 12 ÷ 6 = 2 X 9 = 18
4. 36 ÷ 4 = 9 X 2 = 18 ÷ 6 = 3
5. 5 X 4 = 20 ÷ 10 = 2 X 7 = 14
6. 42 ÷ 7 = 6 X 4 = 24 ÷ 12 = 2

Page 59
1. 78 R3
2. 71
3. 215
4. 57 R1
5. 31 R2
6. 324
7. 186
8. 38 R1
9. 279
10. 66
11. 152
12. 54 R1

Page 60
1. 37 X 2 = 74 ears
2. 114 ÷ 6 = 19 bunnies
3. 116 ÷ 4 = 29 cats
4. 12 X 9 = 108 feathers

Page 61
1. 48 ÷ 12 = 4 shelves
2. 29 X 2 = 58 bowls
3.
```
    17
3 ) 52
    -3
    22
    -21
    1
```
17 cages; 1 bunny remaining
4. 27 X 9 = 243 fish